Let's Make A Haunted House
by Andy Rector

**Illustrated by
Rocky Katz**

It's Halloween.
Let's make a
haunted house!

Mom and Dad said they will help us turn the basement into a haunted house!

Let's put streamers up.

We'll make
signs for the
basement door.

We'll make
jack-o-lanterns
out of pumpkins.

We'll spray
pretend cobwebs
all around the
basement.

We'll hang
decorations on
the wall.

We'll make
a pretend ghost!

Mom will be
a witch stirring up
treats in her
cauldron.

We'll play
scary-sounding
music.

The haunted
house is ready!
Dad tells
scary stories.
Mom brings us
snacks.

Making a haunted house is fun!